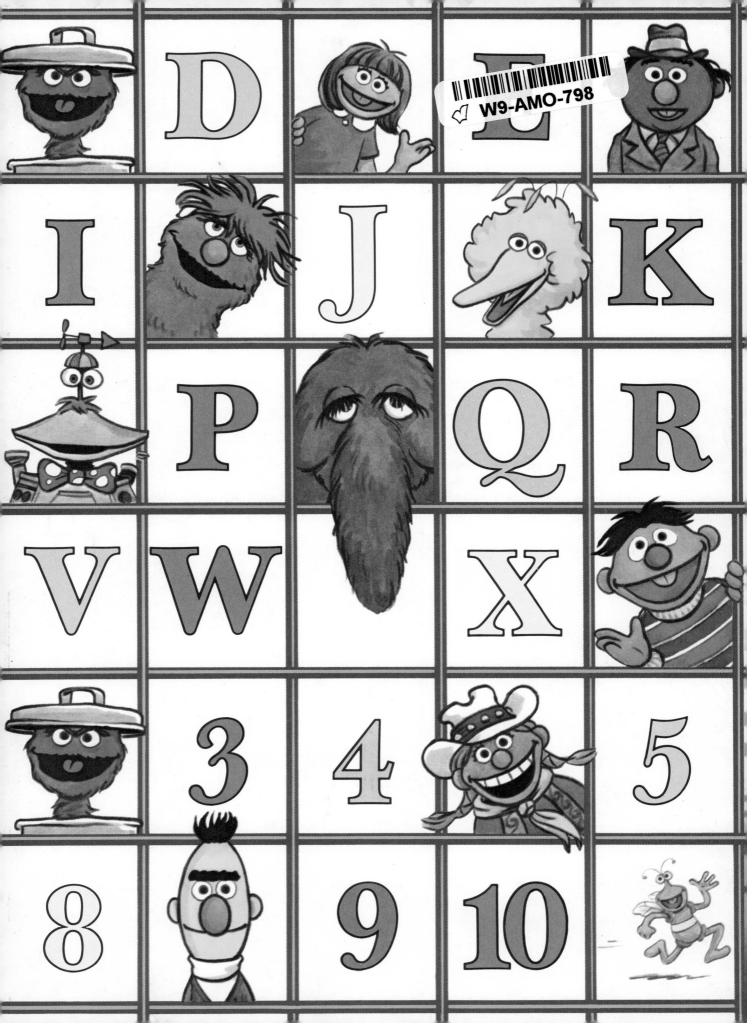

THE SESAME STREET TREASURY

Featuring Jim Henson's Sesame Street Muppets

VOLUME 14

STARRING
THE NUMBER
14
AND THE LETTERS
U, V, AND W

Children's Television Workshop/Funk & Wagnalls, Inc.

WRITTEN BY:

Linda Bove with the
National Theatre of the Deaf
Michael Frith
Jocelyn Gunnar
Emily Perl Kingsley
David Korr
Sharon Lerner
Jeffrey Moss
Norman Stiles
Pat Tornborg
Daniel Wilcox

ILLUSTRATED BY:

Tom Cooke
Mel Crawford
Peter Cross
A. Delaney
Robert Dennis
Mary Grace Eubank
Michael Frith
Tom Herbert
Joe Mathieu
Marc Nadel
Bob Pullin
Maggie Swanson

PHOTOGRAPHS BY:

Charles Rowan
Neil Selkirk
View-Master International Group

Take Uncle Humperdink to visit his nephew, Big Bird, in his nest.

Sesame Street Alphabet

Ernie is in the bathtub watching his bubbles.
Look! Do you see the letters in the bubbles?
What letters do you see? **U**, **V**, and **W**!

There are two kinds of **U**'s. Find this **U**. Find this **u**.

There are two kinds of **V**'s. Find this **V**. Find this **v**.

There are two kinds of **W**'s. Find this **W**. Find this **w**.

Tom Herbert

J. Mathieu

Telly Monster

Home:	456 Sesame Street
Favorite Food:	Bananas
Favorite Drink:	Banana shake
Best Friend:	Oscar the Grouch
Worst Friend:	Oscar the Grouch
Favorite Activities:	Watching TV, French cooking
Favorite TV Show:	<u>Ask Oscar</u>, the Grouch TV show, with co-host Telly Monster
Favorite Shoes:	High-top sneakers
Favorite Wish:	That everything will turn out right
Favorite Saying:	"Anything that can go wrong will go wrong."

The King and the Fireman

Once upon a time, in a palace in a faraway kingdom, there lived a king. Now the king and everybody in his kingdom were living quite happily until one day an awful thing happened. The king's palace caught on fire.

"Oh, my!" yelled the king. "My palace is on fire. Fireman, fireman! Come quick!"

The fireman heard the king yelling and quickly ran to the rescue.

"Here I am, Your Majesty!" cried the fireman. "Ready with my trusty hose!"

He had arrived just in the nick of time, and he put out the fire. Well, the king was so grateful that he immediately issued a royal proclamation:

"I hereby proclaim that from now

on, everyone in my kingdom will quit his or her job and become a fireman!"

So all of the king's subjects quit their jobs and became firemen. Well, it wasn't very long before the king began to have problems. In fact, the very next morning the king was playing with his royal blocks, and he hurt his finger.

"Oh, no!" cried the king. "I've cut my royal finger! Quick, somebody call the Royal Doctor!"

The Royal Doctor was summoned to the king's side. But she didn't *look* like a doctor. She was wearing a fireman's suit.

"I'd like to help you," she said. "I *used* to be a doctor, but I fight fires now. Maybe if I blew my siren your finger would feel better." And she pushed the siren button on her fire

truck. "I hope that helps," she said, and left.

"Boy-oh-boy!" cried the king. "I hurt my royal finger and there's no one to fix it. Only people blowing sirens, so that now my ears hurt, too!"

Well, if that wasn't bad enough, the next day the king was waiting for his mail, and he had another problem.

"Where is my royal mail?" asked the king. "I am expecting a very important royal letter. Where is the Royal Postman? Send for the Royal Postman immediately!"

So the Royal Postman was sent for, but...he arrived wearing a fireman's uniform.

"I'm not a postman anymore," he told the king. "I'd love to help you, but you ordered everyone to be a fireman. So I'm a fireman now."

"But who's going to deliver my mail?" wailed the king.

"I don't know. But...here's a hose. See you around." And he left.

The king was very upset. "I can't read a fire hose!" he grumbled. "I sure wish I had some royal mail to read."

Well, if that wasn't enough, it wasn't long before the king had yet another problem.

"Wow, am I hungry!" said the king. "I'm in the mood for a royal baloney sandwich. Where is the Royal Cook? Royal Cook, bring me my lunch!"

So the Royal Cook was summoned. But when he appeared, he too was dressed as a fireman.

"I used to be the Royal Cook," he said, "but I'm a fireman now, because that's what you ordered."

"But I'm hungry!" yelled the king. "I want a baloney sandwich!"

"I'm sorry," said the cook. "Try eating this." And he handed the king his fireman's hat. "Maybe with a little ketchup it won't taste too bad," he said. And he left.

"Boy-oh-boy-oh-boy!" complained the king. "What kind of a kingdom is this? I'm hungry, but there's no one around but firemen who give me hats to eat. I have a feeling that something's wrong around here."

Well, the king sat and thought, and he realized that he had made a big mistake. So he made a new proclamation:

"I hereby proclaim that everybody should go back to his or her old job, and from now on only firemen should be firemen, and everyone else should just do his or her own thing!"

And the doctor, the postman, the cook, and everybody else immediately took off their fireman suits and started celebrating.

"Now that I'm a doctor again, I can fix your finger!" exclaimed the doctor.

"And now I can deliver the royal mail right away!" cried the postman.

"And here's that royal baloney sandwich you wanted," said the Royal Cook.

And so the king had learned a very important lesson. It takes all kinds of people to make a world, and if everybody had the same job, it would be pretty hard to get things done. It would be pretty silly, too.

Tall and Short Poem
by Big Bird and Little Bird

I wish I were as big as you,
I wish that I were tall.
I'm tired of being overlooked,
I'm tired of being small.

If I were tall, I'd stand up straight
And reach the highest shelf,
And if my toy was stuck up there
I could get it by myself!

I wish that I were short like you,
I wish that I were small.
I tower over everyone,
I'm tired of being tall.

If I were short it would be fun,
I'd never bump my head,
And my feet would not get chilly
'Cause they stick out of my bed.

But sometimes when you're trying to hide,
It's better to be small.

And being tall is not so bad
When playing basketball.

So maybe when we think it out,
What's really best by far
Is finding out what's good about
Being the way you are.

SESAME·TREATS

I THINK YOU'VE MADE A MISTAKE, BIG BIRD. DIDN'T YOU WANT YOUR SIGN TO SAY "SESAME STREET"?

NO, MR. BLOOPER. THIS IS JUST WHAT I MEANT. THIS SIGN IS FOR MY TABLE AT THE BLOCK PARTY. I'M GOING TO BE SELLING SESAME TREATS MADE FROM SESAME SEEDS AND HONEY. TRY A PIECE, MR. COOPER, AND SEE IF YOU LIKE IT.

Sesame Treats

What you need:

1 cup of toasted sesame seeds (If you can't buy them toasted, have a grownup toast them in the oven at 250° for about 10 minutes, until golden.)

$\frac{2}{3}$ cup of honey

What you do:

Have a grownup help you cook the honey in a heavy-bottomed pot until the candy thermometer reads 265°. (Watch the thermometer carefully, because the temperature must be exact.) Then stir in the seeds and mix them well. Take the pot off the stove. Grease a cookie pan, and pour in the honey-seed mixture, spreading it evenly in a layer about $\frac{1}{4}$ inch thick. It will harden as it cools. Then you can break it into bite-size Sesame Treats!

9

FRUTAS Y VEGETALES

FRUITS AND VEGETABLES

Say it in Spanish!

naranjas
oranges

uvas
grapes

manzanas
apples

plátanos
bananas

zanahorias
carrots

tomates
tomatoes

repollo
cabbage

apio
celery

piña
pineapple

bróculi
broccoli

Bert lost 14 pigeons.
Can you help him find them?

"Oh, joy! I, Grover, am the fastest monster on four wheels. And I owe it all to my wonderful little red wagon! Do you like the black and white racing stripes? The stripes are necessary for super speed.

"Notice that my cute little wagon has one, two, three, four, *four* wheels and one handle for steering. I always wear a little hat and scarf when I drive, like the professionals. I, Grover, love the feel of the wind in my face and the sun on my back. Watch out, everybodee! Here I come!!!"

woods

In the Woods

deer

owl

rabbit

turtle

fox

raccoon

skunk

spider

squirrel

frog

bear

How many things in this picture can you "sign"?

Who   lives

in

the woods?

Ernie's Guessing Game

Hey, Bert! Come here. I've got a terrific guessing game.

Oh, good, Ernie. I love guessing games. What do I do first?

Well, you see, I've put a lot of things on the table here. Now I'm going to blindfold you and hand you one of the things and YOU have to guess what it is. O.K.?

But ERNIE! How can I tell what it is if I can't see it?

Oh, easy, Bert. You can feel it with your HANDS, or smell it with your NOSE, or listen to it with your EARS, or taste it with your TONGUE. Here, try this one.

This is going to be fun, Ernie. Hmmmm, this feels sort of smooth with lumps on it. It smells kind of ... SOAPY? It doesn't make ANY noise ...

SQUEEZE it, Bert!

Why, Ernie! It's your RUBBER DUCKIE! Hey, that was fun. Now it's your turn.

QUACK QUACK

Hmmmm. This feels kind of round ... with little bumps on it. It smells ... nice. It doesn't make any noise. Maybe I should TASTE it. Hmmm ... what could it be? I'd better try another one. Nope ... I'll try one more. I can't figure it out. I'll just try another ... and another ... and ...

Ernie— don't you know what it is YET?

Bert, I think I have it! Those were the chocolate-chip cookies you bought for our dessert tonight! They were DELICIOUS!

ERNIE!!! I give up!

If you'd like to play this game, here are some things you can use. And remember—no peeking!

Ball	Book
Bell	Orange
Clock	Spoon, Fork
Keys	Toys
Cup	Cookies
Apple	Pencil
Potato	Crayon
Tomato	Carrot

Grover Gets Wet

Hi! It is your old pal Grover again, here to talk to you about the letter **W**.

Do you know what begins with the letter **W**? **Water** begins with the letter **W**. And this is a big tank of water.

Do you know who lives in this tank of water? Willy the Walrus lives in this tank of water. And his name begins with the letter **W**, too. Oh, this is so much fun.

I will now bend over the top of the tank and see if my cute little eyes can see Willy the Walrus.

WHOOPS!

Whoops also starts with the letter W.

SPLASH

Now I am wet. The word **wet** also begins with the letter **W**. Well, since I am wet, there is one other thing that begins with the letter **W** . . .

WASH!

THE COUNT AT THE TWIDDLEBUG PICNIC
Featuring the Number 14

One sunny April fourteenth, fourteen Twiddlebugs decided to have a picnic. They planned it perfectly—there were fourteen of everything!

Just as they had everything set out for their picnic, along came the Count. "Springtime is wonderful," said the Count, "there is so much to count!"
Suddenly, he spied a tiny tablecloth in the grass. Bending over, he saw fourteen tiny Twiddlebugs having a picnic.

"Wonderful, wonderful!" said the Count. "What a wonderful day for a picnic!"

"Yes," said the Twiddlebugs, "if it doesn't rain, like last year."

"Rain!" said the Count. "Impossible! I could not find a single cloud in the sky to count. Do you mind if I join you?"

"Certainly not," they replied. "But we only have enough for fourteen."

"Fourteen!" cried the Count. "My favorite number! I do not wish to disturb you, I only want to lie here and count. Carry on, carry on with your wonderful picnic."

"Suit yourself," they said.

The Twiddlebugs began to pass around their fourteen jelly sandwiches.

"Aha!" said the Count. "One little jelly sandwich! Two little jelly sandwiches!! Three little jelly sandwiches!!!"

There was a flash of lightning and the sound of thunder as the Count counted the sandwiches. The Twiddlebugs looked up nervously.

"You don't think it will rain, do you?" they asked.

"It is nothing," said the Count. "Do not worry! Eat, little Twiddlebugs, eat! Eight cups of Twiddle punch. Nine cups of Twiddle punch!!....."

The Count counted everything on the Twiddlebug menu, while they worried more and more about the rain.

"Twelve adorable little cupcakes! Thirteen adorable little cupcakes!!" said the Count. "This is so *exciting*! FOURTEEN adorable little cupcakes!!!"

Thunder and lightning crashed around the tiny picnic and the Count kept counting.

The Twiddlebugs were starting to pack up and run home, when one of them cried, "Wait! Wait! We don't have to go home!" And she handed out fourteen little red-and-white-polka-dot umbrellas.

"Look at that!" cried the Count. "I thought that I had counted everything. First I will count the umbrellas, and then I will count the polka dots! One little red-and-white-polka-dot umbrella! Two little red-and-white-polka-dot umbrellas!! *Three* little red-and-white-polka-dot umbrellas!!! Wonderful, wonderful. A wonderful picnic!"

And it was!

The Case of the Mysterious Mud Puddle Monster

One day, Big Bird decided to take a walk around Sesame Street. He opened his door and stepped out—right into a mud puddle. "Oh, drat," he said. "Phooey." But it was too nice a day to fret, so he went on his way, forgetting all about the puddle.

Next he stopped at Mr. Hooper's store for a birdseed soda and an apple. Prairie Dawn was minding the store for Mr. Hooper, and Cookie Monster was also there, having a cookie sandwich. Big Bird drank his soda, ate his apple, and chatted for a while with his friends.

First he went to the home of Oscar the Grouch, who lived in a trash can and collected trash. Big Bird wanted to give him some old papers he had saved. Oscar said, "Swell, now leave me alone," and Big Bird left, happy that Oscar liked his present.

Then he remembered that Ernie and Bert had invited him to come see their new tablecloth, so he decided to visit them. After he had admired the tablecloth, which was covered with blue and white squares, he told Ernie and Bert how much he liked it, and set off for home.

When he got there, he saw Sherlock Hemlock, the world's greatest detective, looking through a magnifying glass at something on the ground.

"Hi, Mr. Hemlock," said Big Bird. "Are you looking for clues with your magnifying glass?"

"Indeed I am, Big Bird," said Sherlock Hemlock. "I, Sherlock Hemlock, the world's greatest detective, am investigating my newest case."

"Oh, boy!" said Big Bird. "What kind of case is it?"

"It's THE CASE OF THE MYSTERIOUS MUD PUDDLE MONSTER," answered Sherlock Hemlock.

"The Mud Puddle Monster!" said Big Bird, feeling just a little frightened. "What's a Mud Puddle Monster?"

"That," said Sherlock Hemlock, "is the mystery. I don't know what a Mud Puddle Monster is. But I'm going to find out, or I'm not Sherlock Hemlock, the world's greatest detective." Sherlock Hemlock pointed his finger at the ground. "I already have some clues," he said. "Look. These are footprints. And do you see where they start? They start right here, at this mud puddle. That means that whoever made these footprints came *out* of the mud puddle! Now, who else would come out of a mud puddle but a Mud Puddle Monster?"

"My goodness, you're clever, Mr. Hemlock," said Big Bird, bending over to look at the muddy footprints and the puddle. "Hmmm," he said thoughtfully. "That looks just like the mud puddle *I* stepped in a little while ago."

"Egad!" said Sherlock Hemlock. "Another clue. When you stepped in this mud puddle, you made the Mud Puddle Monster *mad*. That is why he came out of the puddle."

"He's mad? Do you mean he's mad at *me*?" asked Big Bird, feeling a little more frightened than before.

"Yes, indeed," said Sherlock Hemlock. "He's mad at you. He's also quite large."

"Oh, dear. How can you tell that?" Big Bird wanted to know.

"From his footprints," Sherlock Hemlock told him. "They're enormous. Only someone very, very big could make footprints like that. Now, let us follow them and see where they lead."

Big Bird and Sherlock Hemlock followed the mysterious footprints, which led straight to Oscar's trash can. Big Bird knocked on the lid, and Oscar peeked out. "What do you want now?" he said.

"We're looking for the Mud Puddle Monster," said Big Bird. "Have you seen him? He's great big, all covered with mud, and he's real mad."

"No, I haven't seen him," said Oscar. "But I'll help you look for him. If he's as nice as he sounds, I'll invite him home for dinner."

Big Bird and Sherlock Hemlock and Oscar then followed the footprints right down the street and into Mr. Hooper's store. They asked Cookie Monster and Prairie Dawn if they had seen the Mud Puddle Monster.

"He's great big," said Big Bird, "and all covered with mud, and he's real mad, and he probably has lots of teeth and a nose shaped like a doorknob."

Cookie Monster and Prairie Dawn shook their heads. "I've never heard of a Mud Puddle Monster," said Prairie Dawn. "And I know I've never seen one."

"But he came right into the store," Big Bird insisted.

"Well, we not see him," Cookie Monster said.

"Egad," said Sherlock Hemlock. "Another clue. The Mud Puddle Monster came right into the store and no one saw him. That can only mean one thing. The Mud Puddle Monster is invisible!"

"Oh, no!" said Big Bird, feeling more frightened than ever. "He's invisible! Now what do we do?"

Sherlock Hemlock looked at the footprints through his magnifying glass. "We must keep following the footprints," he said. "Come along. They go right back out of the store."

Cookie Monster and Prairie Dawn decided to come, too. Prairie Dawn hung up a sign that said, "Closed. Back soon—I hope." And they all set off together.

The tracks now led to Ernie and Bert's door. Big Bird suddenly realized something. "Hey! That Mud Puddle Monster went everywhere I did. I went to Oscar's can, Mr. Hooper's store, and Ernie and Bert's apartment, too!"

"Of course," said Sherlock Hemlock. "It is all beginning to add up. He was following you."

Big Bird didn't say anything, but he was as frightened as he'd ever been.

Then Sherlock Hemlock said, "Wait. Here's another clue. The Mud Puddle Monster is still inside Ernie and Bert's apartment. See? The footprints go in, but they don't come out!"

Big Bird knocked loudly on the door. Ernie opened it, and Big Bird said, "Ernie, Ernie, a monster is hiding in your apartment!"

"Oh, dear," said Ernie. "What kind of monster?"

"It's the Mud Puddle Monster," said Big Bird. "He's great big and he's mad and he's all covered with mud."

"He has lots of teeth, too," added Prairie Dawn.

"And a nose like a doorknob," chimed in Cookie Monster.

"And ears like tennis shoes," Big Bird went on, getting more excited.

"You can't see him because he's invisible," Sherlock Hemlock reminded everyone.

"I want to invite him home for dinner!" shouted Oscar.

"This is terrible," said Ernie. "What are we going to do?" And with that, they all began talking at once. Soon Bert came to the door to find out what was going on.

Big Bird pointed to the muddy footprints. "Look, Bert," he said. "Those muddy footprints go into your apartment, and they don't come out again."

"Of course they don't come out again," said Bert. "All the mud came off on our carpet. I've just been cleaning it up. Next time you come to visit us, Big Bird, I wish you would wipe your feet."

"Me?" said Big Bird. "Why? What did I do?"

"I just told you," said Bert. "You got mud all over our carpet when you came to see our new tablecloth. Those are *your* footprints."

"*My* footprints?" Big Bird looked down at his feet. Sure enough, his feet and the footprints were the same size and shape.

Sherlock Hemlock also looked at Big Bird's feet. Then he announced, "Aha! The final clue. I have solved the mystery!" He turned to Big Bird and said, "*You* are the Mysterious Mud Puddle Monster."

"Who?" said Big Bird. "Me?"

"Yes," said Sherlock Hemlock. "I, Sherlock Hemlock, the world's greatest detective, have piled clue upon clue, sifted all the evidence, and arrived with astounding swiftness at the conclusion to another baffling mystery. *You* are the Mud Puddle Monster."

"Oh, dear," thought Big Bird. "How silly. *I'm* not the Mud Puddle Monster. Why, there's probably no such thing as a Mud Puddle Monster." But he didn't tell Sherlock Hemlock that. "After all," he said to himself, "even the world's greatest detective makes mistakes."

"Well," said Sherlock Hemlock, "I must be going now. My job here is finished. Don't thank me. It's all in a day's work." Then he waved good-bye to everyone, turned, and went off, looking about him through his magnifying glass for his next case.

"Phooey," said Oscar. "Some Mud Puddle Monster. I'm going home."

"I'm just glad everything is all right after all," said Prairie Dawn. "Now I can go back to minding Mr. Hooper's store."

"Me come with you, Prairie Dawn," said Cookie Monster. "All the excitement make me hungry."

"Boy," said Ernie. "I think I feel like reading a nice un-scary story with no monsters. What do you say, Bert?"

Bert said he thought that was a good idea.

Big Bird, who was very happy to know he wasn't being followed by a big, angry, muddy monster with a nose like a doorknob, decided to take a nap. "Solving mysteries always makes me sleepy," he said.

A Visit

Here is a picture of me coming to visit
my cousin Bunscombe, the baker.

This is cousin Bunscombe Bird. He
is carrying a delicious birdseed pie.

Another cousin has arrived. Oh goody! It is police
officer Bertha Bird. She is one of my favorites!

Now Fire Chief Bagshot
Bird is here, too.

The last one to come is my cousin
Bathsheba Bird, the doctor.

And here we all are. Isn't it nice that
so many cousins came to call today?

Where Are the Words?

Where there is a picture say the word.

One day, I went to visit my grandmother. She lived very, very far away.

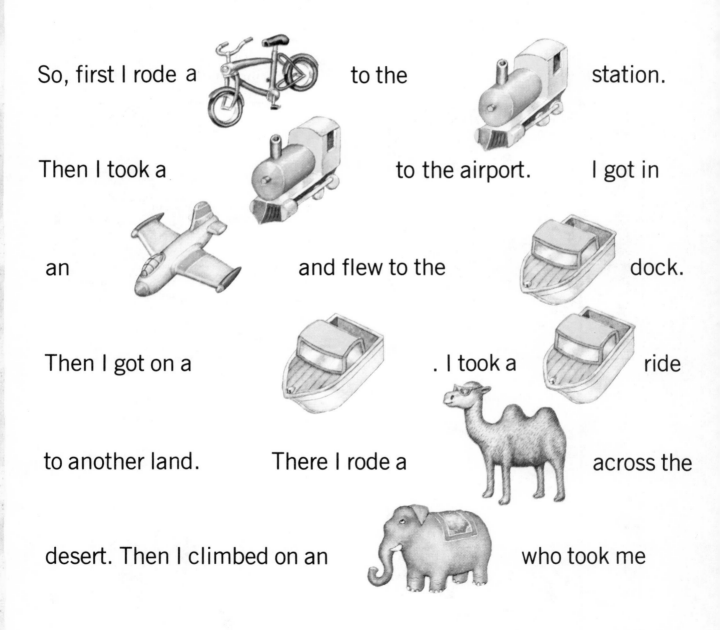

So, first I rode a ⬚ to the ⬚ station.

Then I took a ⬚ to the airport. I got in

an ⬚ and flew to the ⬚ dock.

Then I got on a ⬚ . I took a ⬚ ride

to another land. There I rode a ⬚ across the

desert. Then I climbed on an ⬚ who took me

through the jungle.

Then I rode a  over the hills.

Finally I came to my grandmother's house. She was not home.

So I rode the , then the ,

then the , then the , then

the , then the , then

the until I got all the way home again. Whew!

I opened the door, and there was my grandmother! She had come to visit me! "Where have you been, Grover?" asked my grandmother.

"Oh, around," I said, and I got in her lap and fell asleep.

If that's your idea of wonderful, you'll probably love learning the letters and numbers in volume 15.